Wipe-Clean
Multiplying

Illustrated by Marta Cabrol

Written by Holly Bathie
Designed by Meg Dobbie
and Keith Newell

There are answers, and notes for grown-ups at the back of the book.

Edited by Jessica Greenwell
Series Editor: Felicity Brooks

Two by two

Help Baz count each shoe in the jungle store.
Write how many there are after each pair.

There are ☐ shelves and ☐ shoes on each shelf.

There are ☐ shoes altogether.

| 1 | 2 | 3 | 4 | 5 | 6 | 7 | 8 | 9 | 10 |

Help Cheeky continue counting in 2s along the shelves.

Cheeky

2   4   6   ☐   ☐

☐   ☐   ☐   ☐   ☐

Can you spot a pattern to help you continue the numbers without counting?

☐   ☐   ☐   ☐   ☐

There are ☐ shelves on this page and ☐ things on each shelf.

There are ☐ things altogether.

11   12   13   14   15   16   17   18   19   20

If you can see a pattern in this trail of 5s, try writing the rest of the numbers without counting.

11 12 13 14 15 16 17 18 19 20

Groups of 10

It's the family boat race today. There are 2 boats at the front, each with 10 animals in. Write how many animals there are altogether.

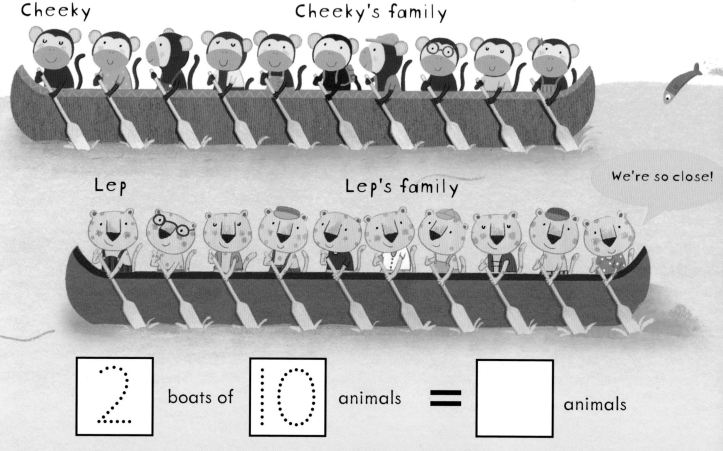

Cheeky   Cheeky's family

Lep   Lep's family

We're so close!

2 boats of 10 animals = ☐ animals

1 more boat of 10 animals is catching up. Write how many animals there are now.

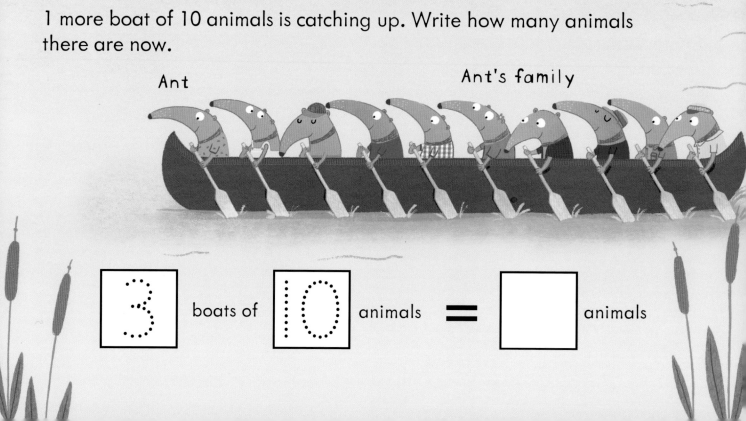

Ant   Ant's family

3 boats of 10 animals = ☐ animals

1 more boat of 10 animals is behind. Fill in the boxes to show how many boats there are now, and how many animals altogether.

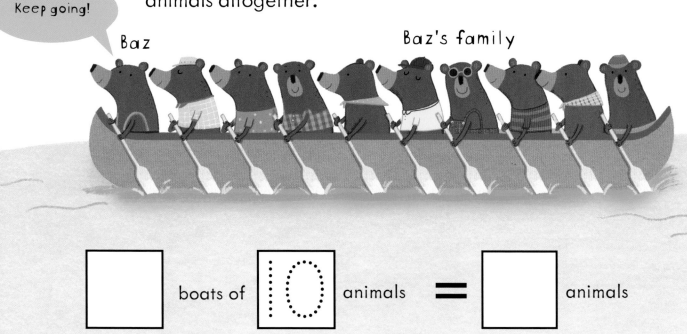

Keep going!

Baz

Baz's family

☐ boats of 10 animals = ☐ animals

If 10 more animals joined, in 1 more boat, how many boats would there be, and how many animals altogether? Fill in the boxes.

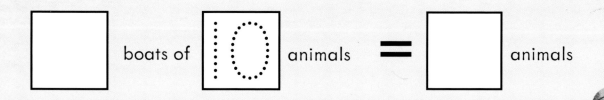

☐ boats of 10 animals = ☐ animals

If another 10 animals joined, in 1 more boat, how many boats would there be, and how many animals altogether? Fill in the boxes.

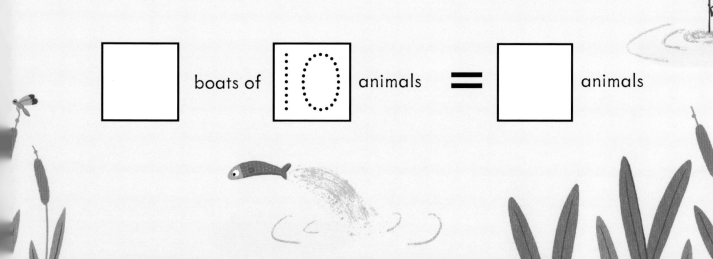

☐ boats of 10 animals = ☐ animals

Three numbers the same

The animals are having a dance competition and the scores are in. Copy the scores into the boxes and write the total score for each couple.

Ten   Ten   Ten

10   10   10

☐ + ☐ + ☐ =

TOTAL SCORE

☐

Three 10s

Five   Five   Five

5   5   5

☐ + ☐ + ☐ =

TOTAL SCORE

☐

Three 5s

□ + □ + □ = TOTAL SCORE □

Three 3s

□ + □ + □ = TOTAL SCORE □

Three 2s

Draw a star next to the couple that has won the dance trophy.

Groups of parrots

The parrots are sitting in groups of 2. Complete the adding calculation to show how many parrots there are altogether.

☐ + ☐ + ☐ = ☐ parrots

Three 2s

When you are adding groups of the same number you can use the multiplying sign. It's also called the "times" sign. Beaky is pointing to it.

X

Squawk!

The parrots have moved into different groups. Can you complete the new calculation?

 X ☐ parrots = ☐ parrots

2 groups of

The parrots have moved into 1 big group.
Complete this calculation.

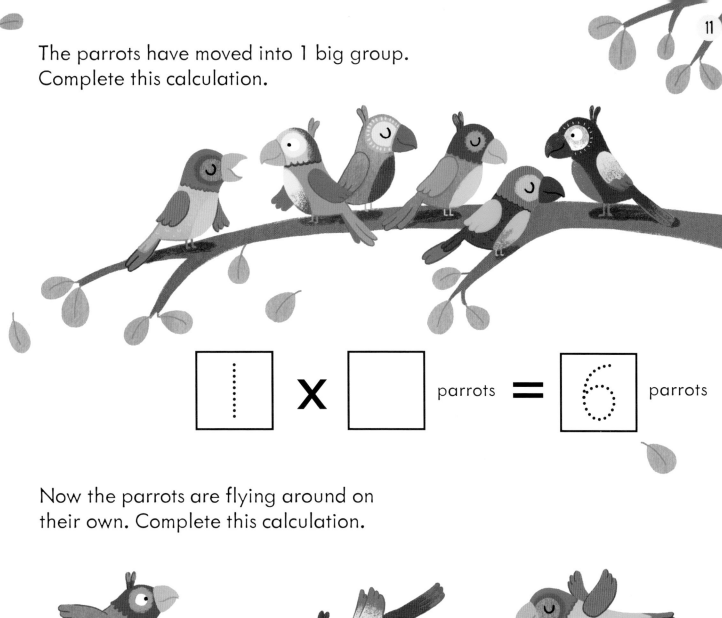

$$\boxed{1} \; \times \; \boxed{} \; \text{parrots} \; = \; \boxed{6} \; \text{parrots}$$

Now the parrots are flying around on
their own. Complete this calculation.

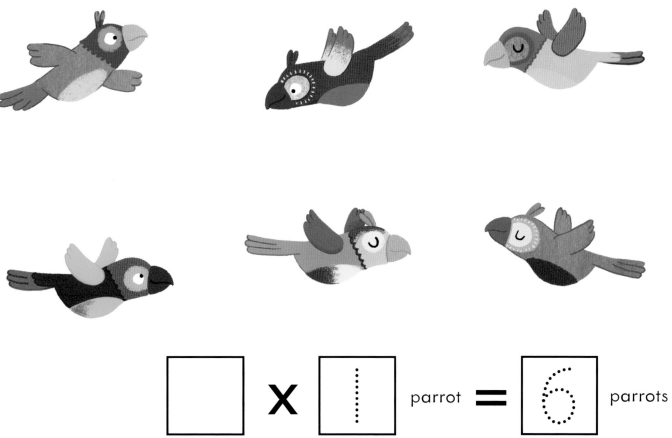

$$\boxed{} \; \times \; \boxed{1} \; \text{parrot} \; = \; \boxed{6} \; \text{parrots}$$

Making groups

Help Ant work out how many butterflies there are.
Circle a group of 4 butterflies. Keep circling groups
of 4 until all the butterflies are in groups.

Write how many groups you have made to complete the calculation.

☐ groups of X ⟦4⟧ butterflies ＝ ⟦20⟧ butterflies

Wipe the butterfly page clean.

Now count the butterflies in groups of 5. Circle groups of 5 butterflies and then complete the calculation.

☐ X ⟦5⟧ butterflies ＝ ⟦20⟧ butterflies

Wipe the butterfly page clean.

Complete the calculations below to show other ways of grouping the butterflies. Remember to wipe the butterflies clean before you start a new calculation.

☐ X ⟦10⟧ butterflies ＝ ⟦20⟧ butterflies

☐ X ⟦2⟧ butterflies ＝ ⟦20⟧ butterflies

☐ X ⟦1⟧ butterfly ＝ ⟦20⟧ butterflies

☐ X ☐ butterflies ＝ ⟦20⟧ butterflies

More multiplying

The animals are playing in the jungle. How many spots are there on these leopards? Complete the calculation.

4 × ☐ spots = ☐ spots

How many monkey ears are there in total below? Complete the calculation.

☐ × 2 ears = ☐ ears

Help the animals with their multiplying calculations.

5 x 10 =

6 x 3 =

2 x 4 =

I think I know the answer.

10 x 5 =

5 x 3 =

This is fun!

3 x 3 =

Spotting patterns

1	2	3	4	5	6	7	8	9	10
11	12	13	14	15	16	17	18	19	20
21	22	23	24	25	26	27	28	29	30
31	32	33	34	35	36	37	38	39	40
41	42	43	44	45	46	47	48	49	50
51	52	53	54	55	56	57	58	59	60
61	62	63	64	65	66	67	68	69	70
71	72	73	74	75	76	77	78	79	80
81	82	83	84	85	86	87	88	89	90
91	92	93	94	95	96	97	98	99	100

The animals are looking for patterns in the number grid.
Help them to draw the patterns.

Draw a circle around each of the numbers in the 2s pattern for me.

It starts 2, 4, 6, 8, 10...

Draw a triangle around each of the numbers in the 5s pattern for me.

It starts 5, 10, 15, 20, 25...

Lep

Look, Tan-tan, the numbers that are in a triangle AND a circle make a new pattern.

Crock

Lem

Oh yes! The new pattern is the pattern of...

Write the answer in the box for me.

Tan-tan

Wipe the grid clean.

Now you could draw circles or triangles for any other patterns you can spot.

Multiplying with 2 and 3

Cheeky and Tig are doing more pattern spotting. Can you see which patterns they have drawn?

1	②△	△3△	④	5	⑥△	7	⑧	△9△	⑩
11	⑫△	13	⑭	△15△	⑯	17	⑱△	19	⑳
△21△	㉒	23	㉔△	25	㉖	△27△	㉘	29	㉚△
31	32	33	34	35	36	37	38	39	40
41	42	43	44	45	46	47	48	49	50

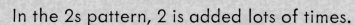

In the 2s pattern, 2 is added lots of times.
The numbers in this pattern are "multiples" of 2.

In the 3s pattern, 3 is added lots of times.
The numbers in this pattern are multiples of 3.

Squawk!

I've drawn a circle around the multiples of 2.
Finish the pattern for me.

I've drawn a triangle around the multiples of 3.
Finish the pattern for me.

12 has a circle AND a triangle around it.
This means it is a multiple of both 2 and 3.

Cheeky has counted in multiples of 2 to 12.
Trace the numbers in her multiplying calculation.

6 x 2 = ☐

I counted 2 six times
to get to 12.
Six sets of 2 is 12.

Tig has counted in multiples of 3 to 12.
Trace the numbers in his multiplying calculation.

4 x 3 = ☐

I counted 3 four times
to get to 12.
Four sets of 3 is 12.

Look for another number in the grid that is a multiple of 2 and 3
and write it in both of the blue boxes below.

☐ x 2 = ☐

☐ x 3 = ☐

Now count in 2s and 3s to complete these two
calculations. You could use the grid to help you.

Wipe
the page
clean

Do the same thing, using the
blue boxes, for the rest of the
numbers in the grid that are
multiples of 2 and 3.

Sorting multiples

These soccer players need to get into their teams.
Write each player's number under the right team
name on the next page.

You could cross out each number on this page as you go.

Multiplying quiz

Find out how much you can remember about multiplying by doing this quiz. Answers on page 24.

A. Ant, Lep and Beaky have forgotten some of the numbers in their patterns. Write the missing numbers in the boxes for them.

Mine is the 2s pattern.

34   36   ☐   40   42   44   ☐

Mine is the 5s pattern.

15   20   25   ☐   35   40   ☐

Mine is the 3s pattern.

9   12   15   18   ☐   24   ☐

B. The animals are adding in their heads to work out how much food they have collected. Show them how they could multiply instead to find the answer – write a multiplying calculation for each animal.

These bananas grow in bunches of 3.

3 + 3 + 3 + 3 + 3 + 3 = ?

☐ X ☐ = ☐

I collected 5 oranges from each tree.

5 + 5 + 5 + 5 + 5 = ?

☐ X ☐ = ☐

These coconuts grow in pairs.

2 + 2 + 2 + 2 + 2 + 2 + 2 = ?

☐ X ☐ = ☐

C. Complete these calculations for Tan-tan and Crock.

9 x 5 = ☐   7 x 3 = ☐   8 x 3 = ☐

3 x 2 = ☐   5 x 5 = ☐   7 x 2 = ☐

2 x 9 = ☐   2 x 8 = ☐   3 x 3 = ☐

5 x 4 = ☐   3 x 5 = ☐   7 x 5 = ☐

10 x 5 = ☐   10 x 2 = ☐

Quiz answers

A. 34   36   38   40   42   44   46   B.   6 x 3 = 18
    15   20   25   30   35   40   45   5 x 5 = 25
     9   12   15   18   21   24   27   7 x 2 = 14

C. 9 x 5 = 45   7 x 3 = 21   8 x 3 = 24   10 x 5 = 50
    3 x 2 = 6   5 x 5 = 25   7 x 2 = 14   10 x 2 = 20
    2 x 9 = 18   2 x 8 = 16   3 x 3 = 9
    5 x 4 = 20   3 x 5 = 15   7 x 5 = 35

Score 1 point for each correct answer and write your score in this box:
If you want to get a higher score, wipe the pages clean and try again.

23